BRAIN ACADEMY
SUPERMATHS

Louise Moore, Pete Crawford
and Richard Cooper

Mission File 5

Years 6-7

Produced in association with

National Association
for Able Children
in Education

Rising Stars are grateful to the following people for their support in developing this series: Sue Mordecai, Julie Fitzpatrick, Johanna Raffan, Belle Wallace and Clive Tunnicliffe.

NACE, The Core Business Centre, Milton Hill, Abingdon, Oxon OX13 6AB
www.nace.co.uk

Rising Stars UK Ltd, 7 Hatchers Mews, Bermondsey Street, London SE1 3GS
www.risingstars-uk.com

Published 2007
Reprinted 2011
Text, design and layout   Rising Stars UK Ltd.

Editorial Consultant: Jean Carnall
Cover design: Burville-Riley
Design: Pentacorbig
Illustrations: Cover – Burville-Riley / Characters – Bill Greenhead

British Library Cataloguing in Publication Data.
A CIP record for this book is available from the British Library.

ISBN: 978-1-84680-234-8

Printed by Craft Print International Ltd, Singapore

CONTENTS

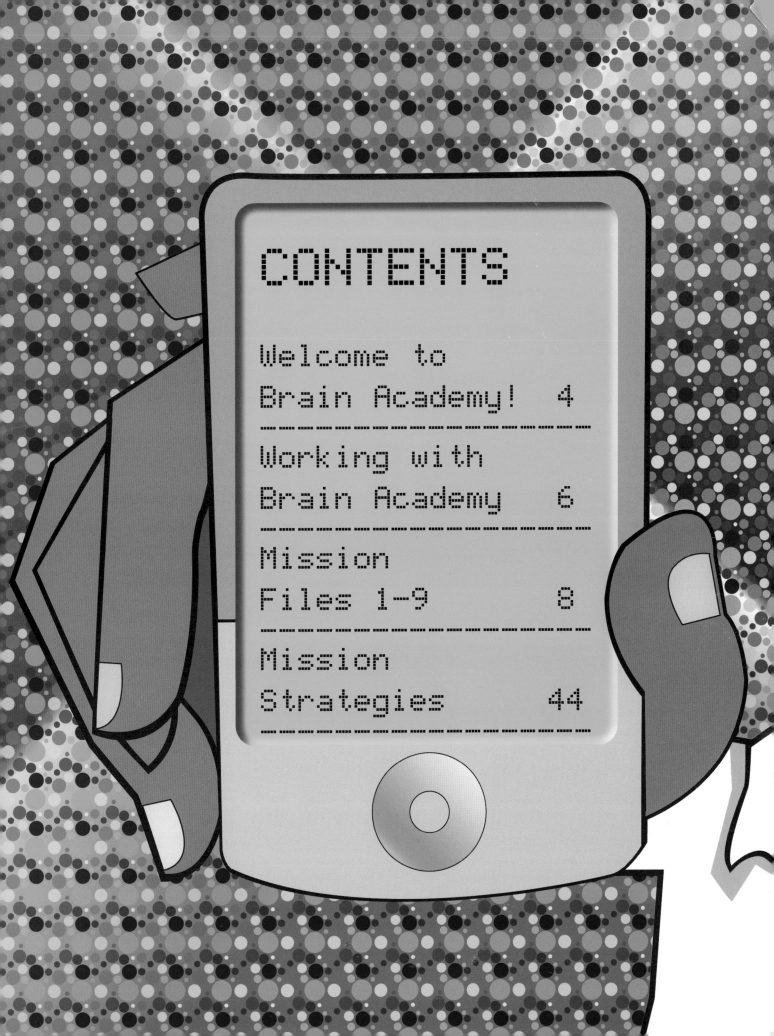

Welcome to Brain Academy!

Welcome to Brain Academy! Make yourself at home. We are here to give you the low-down on the organisation – so pay attention!

It's our job to help Da Vinci and his colleagues to solve the tough problems they face and we would like you to join us as members of the Academy. Are you up to the challenge?

Da Vinci
Da Vinci is the founder and head of the Brain Academy. He is all seeing, all thinking and all knowing – possibly the cleverest person alive. Nobody has ever actually seen him in the flesh as he communicates only via computer. When Da Vinci receives an emergency call for help, the members of Brain Academy jump into action (and that means you!).

Huxley
Huxley is Da Vinci's right-hand man. Not as clever, but still very smart. He is here to guide you through the missions and offer help and advice. The sensible and reliable face of Brain Academy, Huxley is cool under pressure.

Dr Hood
The mad doctor is the arch-enemy of Da Vinci and Brain Academy. He has set up a rival organisation called D.A.F.T. (which stands for Dull And Feeble Thinkers). Dr Hood and his agents will do anything they can to irritate and annoy the good people of this planet. He is a pain we could do without.

Hilary Kumar
Ms Kumar is the Prime Minister of our country. As the national leader she has a hotline through to the Academy but will only call in an extreme emergency. Confident and strong willed, she is a very tough cookie indeed.

General Cods-Wallop
This highly decorated gentleman (with medals, not wallpaper) is in charge of the armed forces. Most of his success has come from the help of Da Vinci and the Academy rather than the use of his somewhat limited military brain.

Mrs Tiggles
Stella Tiggles is the retired head of the Secret Intelligence service. She is a particular favourite of Da Vinci who treats her as his own mother. Mrs Tiggles' faithful companion is her cat, Bond… James Bond.

We were just like you once – ordinary schoolchildren leading ordinary lives. Then one day we all received a call from a strange character named Da Vinci. From that day on, we have led a double life – as secret members of Brain Academy!

Here are a few things you should know about the people you'll meet on your journey.

Inspector Pattern

The trusty Inspector is Buster's right-hand lady. Ms Pattern looks for clues in data and is the complete opposite to the muddled D.A.F.T. agents. Using her mathematical mind to find order where there is chaos, she is a welcome addition to Da Vinci's team. In fact some of the team would do well to think in such a methodical way… a certain Mr Blastov perhaps?

Maryland T. Wordsworth

M.T. Wordsworth is the president of the USA. Not the sharpest tool in the box, Maryland prefers to be known by his middle name, Texas, or 'Tex' for short. He takes great exception to being referred to as 'Mary' (which has happened in the past).

Buster Crimes

Buster is a really smooth dude and is in charge of the Police Force. His laid-back but efficient style has won him many friends, although these don't include Dr Hood or the agents of D.A.F.T. who regularly try to trick the coolest cop in town.

Sandy Buckett

The fearless Sandy Buckett is the head of the fire service. Sandy and her team of brave firefighters are always on hand, whether to extinguish the flames of chaos caused by the demented Dr Hood or just to rescue Mrs Tiggles' cat…

Echo the Eco-Warrior

Echo is the hippest chick around. Her love of nature and desire for justice will see her do anything to help an environmental cause – even if it means she's going to get her clothes dirty.

Victor Blastov

Victor Blastov is the leading scientist at the Space Agency. He once tried to build a rocket by himself but failed to get the lid off the glue. Victor often requires the services of the Academy, even if it's to set the video to record Dr Who.

Prince Barrington

Prince Barrington, or 'Bazza' as he is known to his friends, is the publicity-seeking heir to the throne. Always game for a laugh, the Prince will stop at nothing to raise money for worthy causes. A 'good egg' as his mother might say.

Working with Brain Academy

Do you get the idea? Now you've had the introduction we are going to show you the best way to use this book.

Bazza keeps an eye on things...

Time: During an archaeological dig
Place: Somewhere in Egypt

Prince Barrington has been digging around and found a tablet with some ancient hieroglyphics on it. He is not sure what it is, so he asks Inspector Pattern for some help as she is a keen amateur archaeologist.

Those are Egyptian symbols. The large one in the middle is called the Eye of Horus.

Each part of the Eye of Horus represents a fraction and the Egyptians made different values by adding together parts of the eye, like this:

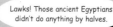 represents $\frac{1}{4} + \frac{1}{2}$ which we would write as $\frac{3}{4}$.

Lawks! Those ancient Egyptians didn't do anything by halves.

$\frac{1}{16}$ $\frac{1}{4}$ $\frac{1}{2}$ $\frac{1}{8}$

$\frac{1}{32}$ $\frac{1}{64}$

24

TM

1) What fractions do these symbols represent?
   For each one, write the parts as an addition statement, then see if you can write the single fraction we would write.

   a)   b)

   c) d)

2) How would you represent these fraction statements using the parts of the eye?
   a) $\frac{1}{4} + \frac{1}{16}$ b) $\frac{1}{16} + \frac{1}{4} + \frac{1}{2}$ c) $\frac{1}{32} + \frac{1}{64}$

3) Write a single fraction for each of the symbols you have drawn.

4) How would you represent these fractions using the parts of the eye?
   a) $\frac{3}{16}$ b) $\frac{15}{16}$ c) $\frac{33}{64}$

5) What is the largest fraction that can be represented by the Eye of Horus?

MM

The Egyptians wrote all their fractions using unit fractions.

Not for the first time, I'm confused. Please explain further, my dear.

The Egyptians only wrote unit fractions. Unit fractions always have the number 1 as their numerator (top number), so they are fractions like $\frac{1}{2}$, $\frac{1}{3}$ and $\frac{1}{4}$.

25

The plot
This tells you what the mission is about.

The Training Mission
Huxley will give you some practice before sending you on the main mission.

Each mission is divided up into different parts.

Each book contains a number of 'missions' for you to take part in. You will work with the characters in Brain Academy to complete these missions.

The Main Mission

This is where you try to complete the challenge.

Huxley's Think Tank

Huxley will give you some useful tips to help you on each mission.

MM

When the Egyptians wanted to write fractions like $\frac{3}{4}$, they added unit fractions together – but they never repeated the same fraction.

So when the Egyptians wrote $\frac{3}{4}$:

- they COULD NOT write $\frac{1}{4} + \frac{1}{4} + \frac{1}{4}$ as it uses more than one $\frac{1}{4}$.
- they COULD write $\frac{1}{2} + \frac{1}{4}$ using two different unit fractions.

1) What fractions could the Egyptians write to complete these additions?

a) $\frac{5}{8} = \frac{1}{2} + \boxed{}$

b) $\frac{5}{16} = \frac{1}{4} + \boxed{}$

c) $\frac{7}{8} = \frac{1}{2} + \boxed{} + 1/8$

d) $\frac{15}{16} = \frac{1}{2} + \boxed{} + \boxed{} + \boxed{}$

HUXLEY'S THINK TANK

- Thinking about equivalent fractions will be helpful.
  For example: $\frac{1}{3} = \frac{2}{6} = \frac{3}{9} = \boxed{\frac{4}{12}} = \frac{5}{15}$
  $\frac{1}{4} = \frac{2}{8} = \boxed{\frac{3}{12}} = \frac{4}{16} = \frac{5}{20}$
  So $\frac{7}{12}$ can be written as $\frac{1}{3} + \frac{1}{4}$

2) What fractions could the Egyptians write to complete these additions?

a) $\frac{5}{6} = \frac{1}{2} + \boxed{}$

b) $\frac{7}{12} = \frac{1}{3} + \boxed{}$

c) $\frac{11}{12} = \frac{1}{2} + \boxed{} + \boxed{}$

d) $\frac{11}{18} = \boxed{} + \frac{1}{6} + \boxed{}$

3) How could the Egyptians write these fractions?

a) $\frac{2}{3}$ b) $\frac{3}{5}$ c) $\frac{4}{9}$ d) $\frac{4}{5}$

26

MM

4) You want to divide 3 bags of rice into 4 equal piles and you have a set of balances.

You know each pile should have $\frac{3}{4}$ of a bag, but how do you weigh that out using the balance? Egyptian fractions can come to the rescue!

$\frac{3}{4} = \frac{1}{2} + \frac{1}{4}$

so each pile can have $\frac{1}{2}$ a bag and a $\frac{1}{4}$ of a bag.

a) How would you weigh exactly $\frac{1}{2}$ a bag using the balance?

b) How would you weigh exactly $\frac{1}{4}$ of a bag using the balance?

5) Explain how Egyptian fractions could help you to divide 7 bags of rice into 8 equal piles using just the balances.

6) Would Egyptian fractions help you to divide 5 bags of rice into 6 equal piles using just the balances? Explain your answer.

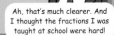

Ah, that's much clearer. And I thought the fractions I was taught at school were hard!

Da Vinci files

Inspector Pattern says there must always be more than one way of writing any fraction in Egyptian fractions? Is she right?

Can any fraction be written in lots of ways using Egyptian fractions? Here is an idea to try:

- You know that $\frac{3}{4} = \frac{1}{2} + \frac{1}{4}$.
- Now write $\frac{1}{4}$ as an addition using unit fractions and rewrite $\frac{1}{2} + \frac{1}{4}$ using your new version of $\frac{1}{4}$.
- Can you write the last fraction of your new version using unit fractions? If you can, then you can write a new addition for $\frac{3}{4}$. Will this keep going?
- Try the same idea for a fraction other than $\frac{3}{4}$. Does it work?
- Do you think Inspector Pattern is right? Give your reasons.

27

No one said this was easy. In fact, that is why you have been chosen. Da Vinci will only take the best and he believes that includes you. Good luck!

PS: See pages 44–47 for some hints and tips and a useful process.

The Da Vinci Files

These problems are for the best Brain Academy recruits. Very tough. Are you tough enough?

7

Pussy patterns

Time: Knitting time
Place: Mrs Tiggles' cottage

Mrs Tiggles is knitting a new woolly 'screen warmer' for Da Vinci and has called on James Bond and his pussy pals to help.

> I can always count on James to lend a paw when I'm knitting. His patterns really are the cat's whiskers!

> Any chance of a new sweater while you're at it, Mrs T?

TM

There are 6 cats altogether, counting James Bond. They sat in a circle and the ball of wool unwound as they rolled it to one another. They always passed the ball in a clockwise direction around their circle.

1) James rolled the ball to the cat on his left, then all the other cats did the same, passing the wool to the cat next to them. The start of this game is shown in the diagram.

Copy the diagram and keep passing the wool until it gets back to James. You don't need to draw the cats, just the dots will do.

What shape have you drawn?

> The cats have been helping Mrs Tiggles with her woolly task. Can you work out what shapes they made? Does it matter where on the circle they start?

TM

2) Mrs Tiggles cleared away the wool, but she was so interested to see what happened that she gave the ball back to James Bond.

This time, the cats passed the ball to the next but one cat (in steps of 2) and carried on until James had the ball again.

What shape did they make this time?

MM

These cats are having a ball! Some of the patterns they're making would look good on the sweater I'm knitting for Huxley.

Two more cats joined the circle, so there were 8 cats altogether. They passed the wool in the same way as before.

1) What shape will they make if they pass the ball in steps of 1, so that each cat passes the ball to the one on its left?

2) What shape will they make if they pass the ball in steps of 2?

3) Mrs Tiggles noticed that when the cats passed the ball in steps of 1, they made an 8-sided shape. When they passed the ball in steps of 2, they made a 4-sided shape. She wondered what shape they would make if they passed the ball in steps of 3.

a) Before you draw anything, what shape do you think they might make? How many sides or corners might it have? Give your reasons for thinking it will be that shape.

b) Now try passing the ball in steps of 3 to find out what happens. Keep going until the ball gets back to James.

c) Describe the shape you have drawn, giving as much detail as you can.

Ask your teacher for a sheet of blank diagrams to use.

HUXLEY'S THINK TANK

- A 5-sided shape is called a pentagon.
- A 6-sided shape is called a hexagon.
- A 7-sided shape is called a heptagon.
- An 8-sided shape is called an octagon.
- A 9-sided shape is called an nonagon.
- A 10-sided shape is called a decagon.

4) Mrs Tiggles loved the last pattern the cats made. She wondered what other patterns they could make with 8 dots so she drew 3 diagrams of her own, firstly joining the dots in steps of 4, then in steps of 5 and finally in steps of 6.

Draw the patterns that she made.

What shapes do you get?

5) Mrs Tiggles tried making patterns with 12 dots.
   What shapes will she get when she joins the dots
   a) in steps of 1?   b) in steps of 2?
   c) in steps of 3?   d) in steps of 4?

6) What steps should she use to join the 12 dots
   to make a straight line?

7) Draw the shapes she makes when she joins the 12 dots:
   a) in steps of 5   b) in steps of 7

   What do you notice? Why do you think this happens?

8) What steps would give the same shape as when you are joining in steps of 4?

9) What would steps of 11 do?

10) Mrs Tiggles then tried an odd number of dots, so she
    drew a circle with 9 dots.

    Without drawing, what shapes do you think she can make?

    Say what steps you think will make each shape.

11) Now try drawing the shape to see if your
    predictions were right.

Da Vinci files

- Without drawing, say what shapes these would give:
  a) 10 dots joined in steps of 2   b) 20 dots joined in steps of 5
  c) 16 dots joined in steps of 12   d) 100 dots joined in steps of 50
  e) 900 dots joined in steps of 300   f) 1,200 dots joined in steps of 1,000

- Choose the number of dots you want around the circle,
  and without drawing, give instructions to make:
  a) a square   b) a straight line   c) a 7-pointed star

One of my friends
swallowed a ball of wool
– she had mittens!

Cods-Wallop's cocktails

Time: A hot afternoon
Place: The local beach

D.A.F.T. agents have decided to spoil the weekend by taking all the drinks from the stalls and cafes at the beach. People are getting all hot and bothered. Hilary Kumar calls for assistance from the army to sort out the problem. General Cods-Wallop agrees to help and springs into action. (Not easy for a man of his age!) On his way to the seaside, he gathers as many ingredients as he can.

It's bringing tears to my eyes already!

My recipe from the Bittabova tribe in the Amazon rainforest ought to sort this lot out, by Jove.

Amazon sour
Put the following into a juicer:
- 4 lemons
- 3 limes
- 2 onions

Stir well. Close eyes and drink!

Whenever I make an Amazon sour, it's important to keep the balance of the ingredients correct. So, every time I use 3 limes, I need 4 lemons and 2 onions. If I use twice as many of one fruit, I need to use twice as many of the other ingredients as well. Can you help?

1) Cods-Wallop used 6 limes to make his first drink.

   a) How many lemons did he use?   b) How many onions did he use?

2) He used 12 lemons to make his next drink.

   a) How many limes did he use?   b) How many onions did he use?

3) He used 12 onions to make his third drink.

   a) How many lemons did he use?   b) How many limes did he use?

4) For his fourth drink, he counted the lemons and limes as he put them into the juicer. When all the lemons and limes were in, he had counted 14 pieces of fruit. How many onions did he then need to add to the drink?

5) He used 36 items to make his final Amazon sour.

   a) How many lemons did he use?

   b) How many limes did he use?

   c) How many onions did he use?

The next drink General Cods–Wallop made was Spicy mango and passion-fruit punch. (Can you see what gives it a punch?)

1) He used 9 chillies for his first drink.

   a) How many passion fruits and mangoes did he use?

2) He used a total of 40 mangoes and chillies to make his next drink.

   How many passion fruits did he use?

3) General Cods-Wallop used between 70 and 80 items for his third drink.

   How many passion fruits, mangoes and chillies did he use?

4) For his fourth drink, he used between 40 and 50 mangoes.

   a) What is the largest number of chillies he could have used?

   b) What is the smallest number of passion fruits he could have used?

5) General Cods-Wallop used 4 litres of lemonade for the first batch of Orange and lime fizzer.

   How many litres of orange juice and lemon barley did he use?

Spicy mango and passion-fruit punch

Put the following into the juicer:

- 5 passion fruits
- 7 mangoes
- 3 chillies

Stand well back before serving!

Always work with whole numbers of each fruit.

Hrrumph! Better make something a little easier on the palate, I suppose.

Orange and lime fizzer

Mix the following:

- 3 parts of orange juice
- 5 parts of lemon barley
- 8 parts of fizzy lemonade

Seal bottle and shake vigorously!

6) The drink sold out so quickly that he decided to make a larger amount.
When he added the orange juice and the lemon barley, he already had
20 litres in the mixer. How many litres of lemonade did he need to add?

7) His final batch of Orange and lime fizzer used up all the ingredients he had
left. When it was made, he had 64 litres of the drink.
How many litres of orange juice, lemon barley and fizzy lemonade did he use?

8) General Cods-Wallop sold out of all of his drinks and had nothing left
to make any more, so he packed up to go home.

a) Before he left, he wanted to know how much money he had made.
He sold 240 drinks altogether and charged 80p for each drink.
How much had he taken?

b) When he got back home, he decided to split the
proceeds between the Retired Generals and the
Old Brigadiers funds. He gave £1 to the OB for
every £2 he gave to the RG. How much money
did he give to each fund?

You've saved the day,
General! D.A.F.T. agents
foiled again.

Da Vinci files

● The General knew that he sold
  - 3 times as many Spicy mango and passion-fruit
    punches as he did Amazon sours.
  - 2 Orange and lime fizzers for every
    Spicy mango and passion-fruit punch.
  - 240 drinks altogether.
● How many of each type of drink did he sell?

industrial products

Time: Late, after work
Place: Hilary's office

Hilary Kumar is working on important paperwork. She is formulating policies with sums and products. Help her ensure that her industries produce the required product by whizzing through some number work with her.

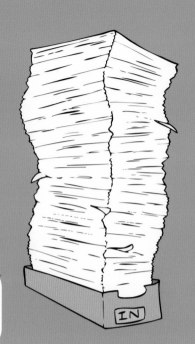

> Look at these lists and figures. I know they are related but I don't have time to sort out how.

> I've got the perfect chap to help here. Huxley!

1) Start by explaining the rules that will tell her if numbers are products of
   a) 2   b) 3   c) 4   d) 5   e) 6

2) Now, we need to look at more complex issues.
   Write some sets consisting of 3 consecutive numbers.

> Hilary needs a quick hand with products, first.

HUXLEY'S THINK TANK

- Consecutive numbers are integers that are next to each other, like 7 and 8.

Try adding the 3 consecutive numbers.

What do you notice about your answers?

What are they all multiples of?

How does the product relate to your 3 consecutive numbers?

Check your findings using other sets of consecutive numbers.

Try using algebra to prove the relationship you have found.

3) a) Huxley lists all the sums that make a total of 4 and finds the product for each sum.

   Here is the start of Huxley's work.

   Now, you complete it.

$$4 + 0 = 4 \dots\dots\dots 4 \times 0 = 0$$
$$1 + 3 = 4 \dots\dots\dots 1 \times 3 = 3$$
$$1 + 1 + 2 = 4 \dots\dots 1 \times 1 \times 2 = 2$$

   What are the maximum and minimum non-zero products of the sums totalling 4?

   Can you use the sums to make a product for every number between the maximum and minimum non-zero products?

b) Continue the study by investigating the products you can make from the sums totalling 5.

   What are the maximum and minimum non-zero products of the sums for 5?

   Can you use the sums to make a product for every number between the maximum and minimum non-zero products?

c) Investigate the products you can make from the sums for 6 and 7.

   What are the maximum and minimum non-zero products for these sums?

   Are there any products between the maximum and minimum that are not possible to make? Explain your findings.

Right! This is starting to make sense! Well done. Now let's step it up a bit.

1) Investigate the products of the sums for other numbers. What do you notice about the non-zero minimum product? Can you find any numbers that give other results? Explain your findings.

2) Hilary needs to create the maximum production for her industries. Look at the sums that gave the maximum products for the numbers you've already investigated.

   a) Investigate the maximum products of the sums for the other numbers up to 10.

b) What do you notice about the sums? Are there any numbers that do not follow the pattern?

c) Explain your findings. Think about what is involved in the pattern and why. Try to make a rule from your findings.

d) Which sums would give the maximum product for 30 and 26?

e) Investigate the maximum products of the sums of numbers up to 20. Write the products in order and explain any patterns you find.

Continue the pattern to give the maximum product of a sum of the number 25.

HUXLEY'S THINK TANK

- When looking for patterns, it is useful to look at the differences between the terms.

Thanks Huxley, that's a big help. Da Vinci has one last challenge!

Hilary's industries manufacture sets of 12 products but are allowed to keep 1 from each set. This means goods are ordered and delivered in sets of 11.

Hilary needs a quick way to work out the multiples of 11 so that she can check the paperwork quickly and efficiently.

- Write the multiples of 11 up to the 20th multiple.
  Devise a rule Hilary can use that only needs addition (not multiplication).

- Use the rule to find the 29th and 88th multiples.
  Check your answers using a calculator.

- Investigate whether your rule works for 3-digit multiples of 11.

From each set of 11 that are delivered, 2 are sent to the emergency store room and 9 are put into general stock.

Now, Hilary needs a quick way to work out the multiples of 9 so that she can check stock levels quickly and efficiently.

- Write the multiples of 9 up to the 30th multiple.
  Devise a rule Hilary can use that only uses addition and/or subtraction.

- Use the rule to find the 35th and 74th multiples.
  Check your answers using a calculator.

- Investigate whether your rule works for 3-digit multiples of 9.

Pigs in paradise

Time: Wee, wee, wee
o'clock in the afternoon
Place: Brain Academy
grounds

Echo thinks it might be useful to keep pigs in the BA orchard as their foraging helps with the maintenance of the woodland and reduces the need for pesticides.

I'm going to experiment with small areas of the orchard and put up fences from tree to tree... But if I could spot a fencing pattern, I'd be able to get these pigs into their new homes much more quickly!

I've asked Inspector Pattern to come over and help you... we could always use a 'sty-scraper' to fit more pigs in!

TM

The trees in the orchard have been planted in a regular pattern, so I've decided to tie my fence from tree to tree.

To begin with, Echo thought there shouldn't be trees inside any section she fences off, just in case the pigs damage them.

These are the sections she fenced off:

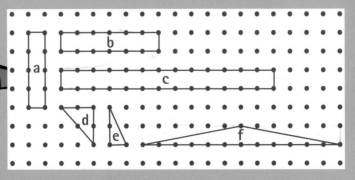

1) What is the area (in squares) of each section?

2) Echo tied the fence to every tree it touched.
How many trees did she tie it to for each section?

3) Inspector Pattern spotted a pattern between the number of trees the fence was tied to and the area it enclosed. What pattern do you think she saw?

HUXLEY'S THINK TANK

- It sometimes helps to write things as a mapping like this:

area		trees touched
1	⟶	4
2	⟶	6
3	⟶	8

4) Echo made these fenced-off sections to check the pattern.

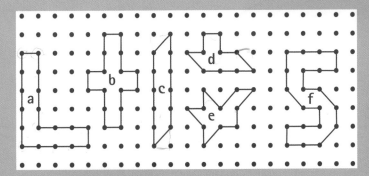

a) She made a table like this. Copy it and fill in the numbers.

Section	a	b	c	d	e	f
Number of trees touched by fence						
Area						

b) Does the pattern still work for these sections?

5) Use squared dotty paper to draw 3 of your own fenced-off sections. Remember, there must be NO TREES INSIDE THE SECTION. Record the areas and number of trees touched for your sections. Does the pattern still hold true?

6) Try these without drawing anything.

a) How many trees will a fence that encloses an area of 15 squares touch?

b) What area will a fence that touches 20 trees enclose?

These porkers need more space – they can have their own 'squeal estate'!

1) Echo thought the sections she had made so far were all quite narrow inside, so she decided to include trees inside the sections to make them wider.

These are the new sections she fenced off:

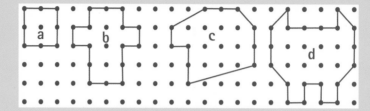

Echo made a new table for these sections.
Copy her table and fill in the numbers.

Section	a	b	c	d
Number of trees touched by fence				
Number of trees inside the section				
Area				

2) Echo wondered if there was a pattern in these results. Inspector Pattern suggested she might find it easier to spot if she kept the same number of trees touching the fence and just altered the number of trees inside.

So Echo kept 4 trees touching the fence and increased the number of trees by 1 each time. Here are the first 3 sections that she made:

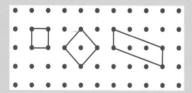

a) Copy Echo's sections onto squared dotty paper, then draw the next 3 sections for her, making sure that 4 trees are touching the fence and the number of trees inside increases by 1 each time.

b) Make a table of results for all 6 sections.

c) What happens to the area each time a tree is added inside?

3) Now try the same idea with 6 trees always touching the fence. Draw sections with 0, 1, 2, 3 and 4 trees inside and record your results in a table. What happens to the area each time a tree is added?

4) What is the link between the number of trees touched by the fence, the number of trees inside the section and the area of the section? Does the connection still work for all the sections in question 1?

5) Use squared dotty paper to draw 3 of your own fenced-off sections. Choose any number of trees you want – on the fence and inside. Does the link between touching trees, inside trees and area still work?

6) Without drawing anything, explain what areas these sections will enclose:

a) a fence that touches 12 trees and has 5 trees inside

b) a fence that touches 17 trees and has 8 trees inside

7) Check your answers to question 6 by drawing sections with the right numbers of touching trees and trees inside.

Are their areas what you predicted?

Fantastic work everyone. Hogs and kisses all round!

Da Vinci files

- What is the largest area you can enclose using a total of 12 trees? Make sure the number of touching trees and the number of trees on the inside will actually make a fenced-off section! E.g. 1 touching tree and 11 trees inside seems to give a large area, but it won't work as you need more than 1 touching tree to enclose an area.

- Would the largest area that a total of 6 trees could enclose be half of the largest area that a total of 12 trees could enclose?

Bazza keeps an eye on things...

Time: During an archaeological dig
Place: Somewhere in Egypt

Prince Barrington has been digging around and found a tablet with some ancient hieroglyphics on it. He is not sure what it is, so he asks Inspector Pattern for some help as she is a keen amateur archaeologist.

> Those are Egyptian symbols. The large one in the middle is called the Eye of Horus.

> Each part of the Eye of Horus represents a fraction and the Egyptians made different values by adding together parts of the eye, like this:
> represents $\frac{1}{4} + \frac{1}{2}$ which we would write as $\frac{3}{4}$.

> Lawks! Those ancient Egyptians didn't do anything by halves.

1) What fractions do these symbols represent?
   For each one, write the parts as an addition statement,
   then see if you can write the single fraction we would write.

a)

b)

c)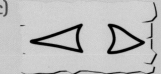

d)

2) How would you represent these fraction statements using the parts of the eye?

a) $\frac{1}{4} + \frac{1}{16}$

b) $\frac{1}{16} + \frac{1}{4} + \frac{1}{2}$

c) $\frac{1}{32} + \frac{1}{64}$

3) Write a single fraction for each of the symbols you have drawn.

4) How would you represent these fractions using the parts of the eye?

a) $\frac{3}{16}$

b) $\frac{15}{16}$

c) $\frac{33}{64}$

5) What is the largest fraction that can be represented by the Eye of Horus?

The Egyptians wrote all their fractions using unit fractions.

Not for the first time, I'm confused. Please explain further, my dear.

The Egyptians only wrote unit fractions. Unit fractions always have the number 1 as their numerator (top number), so they are fractions like $\frac{1}{2}$, $\frac{1}{3}$ and $\frac{1}{4}$.

When the Egyptians wanted to write fractions like $\frac{3}{4}$, they added unit fractions together – but they never repeated the same fraction.

So when the Egyptians wrote $\frac{3}{4}$:

- they COULD NOT write $\frac{1}{4} + \frac{1}{4} + \frac{1}{4}$ as it uses more than one $\frac{1}{4}$.
- they COULD write $\frac{1}{2} + \frac{1}{4}$ using two different unit fractions.

1) What fractions could the Egyptians write to complete these additions?

a) $\frac{5}{8} = \frac{1}{2} + \boxed{}$

b) $\frac{5}{16} = \frac{1}{4} + \boxed{}$

c) $\frac{7}{8} = \frac{1}{2} + \boxed{} + 1/8$

d) $\frac{15}{16} = \frac{1}{2} + \boxed{} + \boxed{} + \boxed{}$

HUXLEY'S THINK TANK

- Thinking about equivalent fractions will be helpful.

   For example: $\frac{1}{3} = \frac{2}{6} = \frac{3}{9} = \boxed{\frac{4}{12}} = \frac{5}{15}$

   $\frac{1}{4} = \frac{2}{8} = \boxed{\frac{3}{12}} = \frac{4}{16} = \frac{5}{20}$

   So $\frac{7}{12}$ can be written as $\frac{1}{3} + \frac{1}{4}$

2) What fractions could the Egyptians write to complete these additions?

a) $\frac{5}{6} = \frac{1}{2} + \boxed{}$

b) $\frac{7}{12} = \frac{1}{3} + \boxed{}$

c) $\frac{11}{12} = \frac{1}{2} + \boxed{} + \boxed{}$

d) $\frac{11}{18} = \boxed{} + \frac{1}{6} + \boxed{}$

3) How could the Egyptians write these fractions?

a) $\frac{2}{3}$ b) $\frac{3}{5}$ c) $\frac{4}{9}$ d) $\frac{4}{5}$

4) You want to divide 3 bags of rice into 4 equal piles and you have a set of balances.

You know each pile should have $\frac{3}{4}$ of a bag, but how do you weigh that out using the balance?
Egyptian fractions can come to the rescue!

$$\frac{3}{4} = \frac{1}{2} + \frac{1}{4}$$

so each pile can have $\frac{1}{2}$ a bag and a $\frac{1}{4}$ of a bag.

a) How would you weigh exactly $\frac{1}{2}$ a bag using the balance?

b) How would you weigh exactly $\frac{1}{4}$ of a bag using the balance?

5) Explain how Egyptian fractions could help you to divide 7 bags of rice into 8 equal piles using just the balances.

6) Would Egyptian fractions help you to divide 5 bags of rice into 6 equal piles using just the balances? Explain your answer.

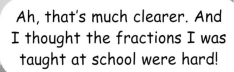

Ah, that's much clearer. And I thought the fractions I was taught at school were hard!

Da Vinci files

Inspector Pattern says there must always be more than one way of writing any fraction in Egyptian fractions? Is she right?

Can any fraction be written in lots of ways using Egyptian fractions? Here is an idea to try:

- You know that $\frac{3}{4} = \frac{1}{2} + \frac{1}{4}$.

- Now write $\frac{1}{4}$ as an addition using unit fractions and rewrite $\frac{1}{2} + \frac{1}{4}$ using your new version of $\frac{1}{4}$.

- Can you write the last fraction of your new version using unit fractions? If you can, then you can write a new addition for $\frac{3}{4}$. Will this keep going?

- Try the same idea for a fraction other than $\frac{3}{4}$. Does it work?

- Do you think Inspector Pattern is right? Give your reasons.

Math-e-magics!

Buster Crimes wants to know how Dr Hood is
getting hold of top secret facts and figures.
No one seems to know and they are not very
interested. Everyone is talking about the latest
magic act appearing at the Brain Academy.

That magician freak is
stealing our secrets, dude!

That's no ordinary magician – he's
doing math-e-magics! I'll help you
understand what he is doing.

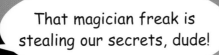

Think of a number between 1 and 10 but don't tell me what
it is. Add 3 to your number, then multiply the answer by 5.
Double your answer. Now divide by 10 and subtract the
number you started with. And I know your answer!

1) Try starting with different numbers between 1 and 10.
What do you notice about the answer?
Why do think that happens?

Work through the puzzle one step at a time, writing
down all the sums you do.

Can you explain how this puzzle works?

Try starting the puzzle with a letter instead
of a number. Work through it a step at a
time, writing down exactly what you do.
What answer do you get this time?

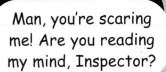

Man, you're scaring
me! Are you reading
my mind, Inspector?

Using letters is an excellent way to prove things in maths. If you can do this you can graduate as an Algebra Ace.

2) Take a look at Inspector Pattern's next trick.

Try this. Think of a number between 1 and 10, add 13, multiply by 2, subtract 6, halve it, add 5 and then subtract your original number. I know your answer again!

Now try it out, starting with different numbers between 1 and 10. Keep a record of the numbers you start with and the answers you get.

Also, try it with numbers between 10 and 50, then with numbers greater than 100 and greater than 1,000. What do you find?

How do you think this trick works?

Write down each step of the problem and show all your working out. Using your working out, can you explain how the trick works?

Way to go girl! You're one smart cookie.

HUXLEY'S THINK TANK

- Instead of starting the tricks with a number, try starting them with a letter.
- Use algebra to work through the problems.

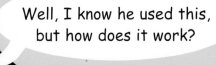

1) Dr Hood has been finding out how many people live in different houses by using a crafty math-e-magic trick.

Well, I know he used this, but how does it work?

Choose a number between 1 and 10. Add 20 and subtract the number of people who live in your house. Multiply by 10 and subtract 100. Halve the answer. Divide by 5 and subtract your original number.

a) Work through the trick and write down the answer. Test it with different numbers. Compare the numbers you started with and the answers you get.

   What do you notice?

b) How do you think this trick works? Write down each step of the problem and show all your working out.

   Using your working out, can you explain how the trick works?
   When you know, test it on different people.

2) Dr Hood has been using similar mathematical tricks to steal people's identities.

Follow these instructions to find out how he discovered peoples' ages and months of birth.

Start with your age, multiply it by 20 and add 40. Multiply the answer by 5 and add the month of your birth (e.g. January = 1). Finally, subtract 200. Tell me your answer and I will tell you your age and the month of your birth.

   a) Work through the trick with your age and month of birth. Write down the answer you get.

b) Test the trick on different people. You may want to use some of the people shown here.

Mary
Age 13
Born in April

Anne
Age 16
Born in August

James
Age 24
Born in December

Isaac
Age 11
Born in November

Jaz
Age 9
Born in July

What do you notice about the numbers you started with and your answers?

How do you think this trick works? Write down each step and see if you can explain it.

Now we've cracked his code, the number's up for that pesky doctor.

Da Vinci files

- Make up your own trick that always gives the same answer.

  Put in about 6 steps – this is enough to confuse the audience so they don't know what is happening, but not too many for you to remember. Make sure the maths isn't too difficult for people to work out mentally.

  When you are sure your trick works, test it on different people. Use algebra to prove how and why it works.

- Make up a trick where the answer will tell you the number of the house where a person lives.

  Use algebra to prove how and why your trick works.

Speculate to tessellate

Time: To re-tile Barrington Hall
Place: Bazza's hallway

All those charity balls that Bazza has hosted over the years have worn away his flooring. It's time for a little home improvement, so he calls the Academy.

> I love the tessellation job the Academy did on my driveway – any chance you chaps can do the same in my ballroom? All those nights on the tiles have worn away my floor!

> We can't have you slip sliding away, Prince!

TM

> I know that square tiles will tessellate (fit together leaving no gaps), but it's a bit boring for a chap-about-town like myself! I'm thinking triangular tiles might be more fitting for a fashion-conscious Princeliness like me.

1) Trace the following triangle and see if it tessellates. If it does, show a reasonable amount of the pattern it makes.

2) Do the same with these triangles.

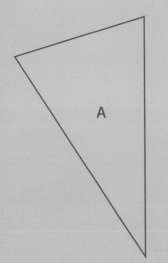

A

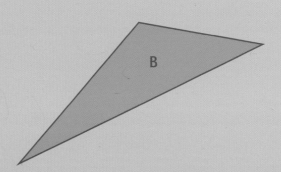

B

3) Draw your own triangle and see if it will tessellate.

4) Do you think that any triangle will tessellate? What reasons do you have or is it just a feeling?

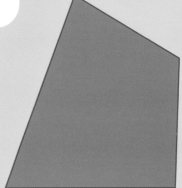

Hmm, now I'm not sure I like any of the triangular patterns... Let's go back to quadrilaterals – but no squares, please!

1) Will this tile tessellate? Trace the quadrilateral and see if it does. If it does, show a reasonable amount of the pattern it makes.

2) Do the same with these quadrilaterals.

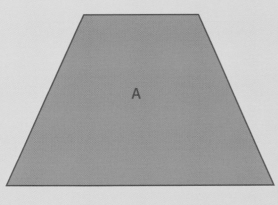

A

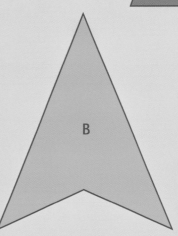

B

3) Draw your own quadrilateral and see if it will tessellate.

4) Try to draw a quadrilateral that will NOT tessellate.

5) Do you think any quadrilateral will tessellate?
What are the reasons for your answer or is it just a feeling?

6) Huxley showed Prince Barrington a way of tessellating a quadrilateral that he thinks will work with any quadrilateral. He drew an awkward one to try.

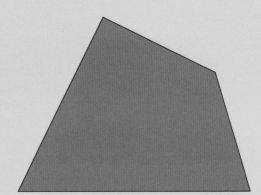

a) Trace Huxley's shape, cut it out and follow his instructions.

Draw around the shape. Then put your pencil on the mid-point of the right-hand side.

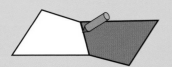

Spin the quadrilateral through half a turn using the pencil as a pivot. Draw around the shape in its new position.

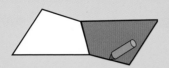

Put your pencil on the mid-point of the bottom line of the shape.

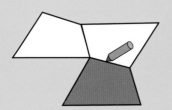

Spin the quadrilateral through half a turn using the pencil as a pivot. Draw around the shape in its new position.

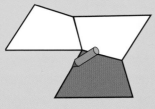

Put your pencil on the mid-point of the left-hand side of the shape.

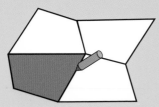

Spin the quadrilateral through half a turn using the pencil as a pivot. Draw around the shape in its new position.

b) Which side could you use next?

c) Will Huxley's method keep going so that the tessellation gets larger?

7) Draw your own quadrilateral. Make it whatever shape you like. See if your quadrilateral will tessellate using Huxley's method.

8) Try to draw a quadrilateral that will NOT tessellate using Huxley's method.

9) Do you think that Huxley was right when he said all quadrilaterals will tessellate?

What about making the tiles out of glass and putting coloured lights underneath? Let's go disco, baby!

Da Vinci files

- Mark each corner of your copy of Huxley's quadrilateral with a different colour.

  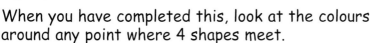

  Use the marked shape on your tessellation, moving it around in the same way as before.

  Each time you place your shape in a new position, mark the pattern with the colours from your shape. Make sure that they are in the right positions:

  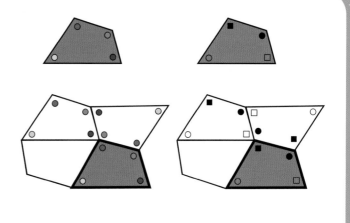

  When you have completed this, look at the colours around any point where 4 shapes meet.

  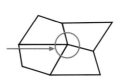

  a) What do you notice?
  b) What does this tell you about the 4 angles of the quadrilateral?
  c) Will it always happen whatever shape quadrilateral you use? Try another one!

- Do the same with one of your triangles.

  What can you say about the 3 angles of the triangle?

Meet the aliens

Time: To start worrying...
Place: Mission control

Victor Blastov is being sent on a mission in his new rocket – Kaputnik. As usual with our Victor, there are a lot of things that could go wrong.

You are likely to meet some strange creatures on the way.

Ja, I need to know ze probability of encountering dangers on ze way. Vot is ze answer?

Ah... well... we don't exactly know all the dangers till you get there.

Don't worry, Huxley will show you the necessary steps to take.

At the first stop on the mission, Victor meets 10 extra-terrestrials. They all look the same to him, so he makes some notes in a table to help him to tell them apart.

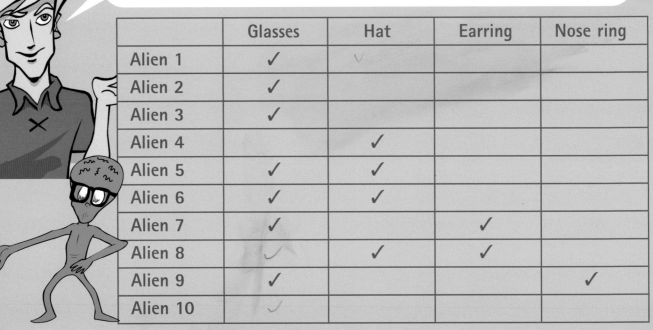

	Glasses	Hat	Earring	Nose ring
Alien 1	✓	✓		
Alien 2	✓			
Alien 3	✓			
Alien 4		✓		
Alien 5	✓	✓		
Alien 6	✓	✓		
Alien 7	✓		✓	
Alien 8	✓	✓	✓	
Alien 9	✓			✓
Alien 10	✓			

If 1 visitor is picked at random, work out the probabilities for these events:

1) a) that a hat is worn   b) that a hat is not worn

2) a) that glasses are worn   b) that glasses are not worn

3) a) that earrings are worn   b) that earrings are not worn

4) a) that a nose ring is worn   b) that a nose ring is not worn

5) Look at your answers to each question, from numbers 1 to 4. Can you find a relationship between the probabilities that something is worn or not worn? Explain any relationships you find.

6) At the next stop, Victor sees some more aliens. From this group, 1 alien is selected at random to meet him. Use the relationships you found previously to help you solve these problems.

     a) If 2 out of 8 aliens have poisonous fangs, what is the probability that the alien Victor met won't have poisonous fangs?

     b) If the probability of an alien having a zapper is 5 out of 12, what is the probability that the alien Victor met doesn't have a zapper?

     c) If 7 out of 20 aliens can communicate with people, what is the probability that the alien Victor met can't communicate with people?

7) Make up at least 5 examples of your own that prove this relationship.

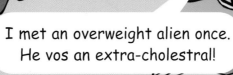

I met an overweight alien once. He vos an extra-cholestral!

At the final stop, Victor Blastov encounters another group of extra-terrestrials. He discovers that the more eyes they have, the more dangerous they are.

One alien is chosen at random to deal with the stranger who has arrived.

1) a) What is the probability that the alien chosen has 3 eyes?
   b) What is the probability that the alien has 7 eyes?
   c) What is the probability that the alien has either 3 eyes or 7 eyes?

2) a) What is the probability that the alien chosen has 5 eyes?
   b) What is the probability that the alien has 6 eyes?
   c) What is the probability that the alien has either 5 eyes or 6 eyes?

3) a) What is the probability that the alien chosen has 9 eyes?
   b) What is the probability that the alien has 7 eyes?
   c) What is the probability that the alien has either 9 eyes or 7 eyes?

4) a) What is the probability that the alien chosen has 3 eyes?
   b) What is the probability that the alien has 6 eyes?
   c) What is the probability that the alien has either 3 eyes or 6 eyes?

I vos captured by teddy-bear-like aliens vonce. It vos a close encounter of ze furred kind!

5) Can you find a relationship between the probabilities in each question? Explain the relationship you find.

Is the relationship still true if there are 3 options?
Give at least 3 examples to support your answer.

6) Use the relationship you discovered above to solve these problems.

a) 4 out of 7 aliens have supersonic hearing. 1 out of 7 of the aliens are deaf. What is the probability that an alien chosen at random has supersonic hearing or is deaf?

b) 5 out of 24 aliens live on Mars. 7 out of 24 live on Pluto. What is the probability that an alien chosen at random lives on Mars or Pluto?

c) Make up at least 5 examples of your own that prove this relationship.

Zose aliens don't scare me. I'm more worried about telling Hilary zat I've left ze bath taps running back home!

The pattern should help you find the relationship you need.

Da Vinci files

- Use this group of spaceships.

Investigate the relationship between the probability that the spaceships have one particular feature or another, and then the probability that a ship has both features.

You could start by investigating spaceships with windows, then spaceships with wings and finally spaceships with windows and wings.

Choose other features to investigate and explain any relationships you find.

Beetle mania!

Time: The 1960s
Place: Liverpool

Dr Hood has bred a new type of beetle that eats butterfly eggs. His evil plan is to destroy the wildlife sanctuaries that Echo has been cultivating for the last few years.

> That scheming Dr Hood must be stopped, otherwise all our work will be ruined. These beetles are spreading like wildfire. Help!

> We need more information on this fiendish beetle to save the butterflies. We can work it out, Echo... but we need to act fast!

TM

> I've been recording the number of beetles in a city street.

1) Take a look at the chart.

Day	1	2	3	4	5	6
Number of beetles	3	5	7	9	11	13

a) On Day 1, there are 3 beetles. On Day 2, there are 5 beetles. How many beetles are there on Day 3?

b) How many beetles will there be on Day 10?

c) What is the relationship between the number of the day and the number of beetles?

d) Use this relationship to work out how many beetles there will be on the 100th day.

2) Echo has been recording the number of beetles in a park.

Day	1	2	3	4	5	6
Number of beetles	1	4	9	16	25	36

a) How many beetles are there on Day 4?

b) How many beetles will there be on Day 10?

c) What is the relationship between the day and the number of beetles?

d) Use this relationship to work out how many beetles there will be on the 100th day.

3) Echo has been recording the number of beetles in a garden.

Day	1	2	3	4	5	6
Number of beetles	4	7	10	13	16	19

a) How many beetles are there on Day 6?

b) How many beetles will there be on Day 10?

c) What is the relationship between the day and the number of beetles?

d) Use this relationship to work out how many beetles there will be on the 100th day.

4) Echo has been recording the number of beetles in a field.

Day	1	2	3	4	5	6
Number of beetles	3	6	11	18	27	38

a) How many beetles are there on Day 6?

b) How many beetles will there be on Day 10?

c) What is the relationship between the day and the number of beetles?

d) Use this relationship to work out how many beetles there will be on the 100th day.

HUXLEY'S THINK TANK

- Think about square numbers for this last question.

These beetles are becoming a real nuisance.
Won't you please, please help me and I'll feel fine!

As the beetles reproduce, they move into new areas.

1) In Buxworth, the beetles always move south. Echo split the area in triangles and recorded which triangles were contaminated each week.

Using isometric paper, draw the smallest possible triangle on the paper.

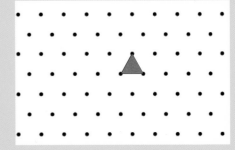

Week 1: 1 triangle contaminated

Area 2 is made of all the triangles that touch the base of the first triangle, even if it's just a corner.

Keep increasing the areas in the same way.

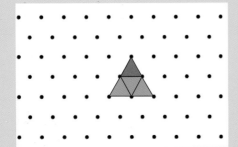

Week 2: 4 triangles contaminated

Keep going until you have spotted the pattern in the number of triangles used.

a) Explain the pattern.

b) Look for a relationship between the number of the week and the number of triangles that are contaminated.

c) Write the relationship using 'W' for the number of the week and 'T' for the number of triangles that are contaminated.

d) Use the relationship to work out how many weeks it would be before 4,000 triangles are contaminated.

2) In Essex, the beetles spread in all directions. Echo started with a hexagon made of 6 triangles. Use isometric paper to draw the hexagon.

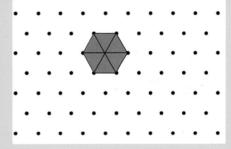

Week 1: 6 triangles contaminated

Area 2 is made of all the triangles that touch the edges of the first hexagon, even if it's just a corner. Keep increasing the areas in the same way.

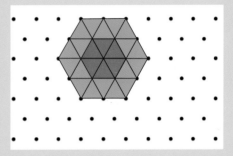

Week 2: 24 triangles contaminated

a) Try to find a relationship using 'W' for the number of the week and 'T' for the number of triangles contaminated.

b) How many weeks would it be before 4,000 triangles are contaminated?

> I think we have enough info on these beetles now to sort them out... with a little help from my friends!

Da Vinci files

Echo decides to investigate the rate of contamination when beetles spread in every direction.

- Investigate how the contaminated area will increase if she splits an area into squares.
- What if she splits the area into triangles and starts with 1 triangle? Hint: the second area isn't a triangle!
- Investigate other shapes. Can you find a relationship between the number of sides in the starting shape and the rate of contamination?

Mission Strategies

MISSION FILE 5:1
You can work out a lot of things about the patterns from the number of dots around the circle and the steps that the ball is passed in. For example, if there are 6 dots around the circle, passing the ball in steps of 2 will get the ball back to the start position in one go around the circle because 2 will divide exactly into 6. As $6 \div 2 = 3$, the shape formed will have 3 corners. But if there are 7 dots around the circle, passing in steps of 2 will not get back to the start in one go around the circle as 2 will not divide exactly into 7... and you can't have a shape with 3 corners!

MISSION FILE 5:2
Some questions only tell you the total number of 2 or more items in a drink.
For example, the Main Mission question 2 tells you that the drink had 40 mangoes and chillies altogether. The recipe says you need 7 mangoes and 3 chillies, so the total number of mangoes and chillies in the menu is 10. As the General put 40 in the drink, he must have used 4 times the numbers in the recipe, so he will need 4 times as many passion fruits as shown in the recipe.

MISSION FILE 5:3
Remember that product has a similar meaning to multiply. You need to work carefully with these lists of sums. If you miss some out, you won't find the patterns you need. Patterns are the key to this Mission – persevere until you find some. Think about multiples, primes and differences when you are pattern hunting. There are useful rules in the Da Vinci Files – spot the patterns!

MISSION FILE 5:4
If you can't spot a pattern from the examples you are given, try drawing some more shapes of your own to give yourself more results to look at. It can be a good idea to draw smaller shapes to begin with so that the numbers aren't too large. Then, if you spot a pattern, you can try some larger shapes to check it out.

MISSION FILE 5:5
When you want to write a fraction such as $\frac{7}{8}$ in Egyptian style, you might find it helpful to list some different fractions that are 8ths and see which ones will cancel into unit fractions. E.g. $\frac{1}{8}$, $\frac{2}{8} = \frac{1}{4}$, $\frac{3}{8}$, $\frac{4}{8} = \frac{1}{2}$
(Why is there no point in trying any numerator larger than 4?)

Then you can see which fractions will go together to make $\frac{7}{8}$. In this case, $\frac{4}{8} + \frac{3}{8}$ or $\frac{4}{8} + \frac{2}{8} + \frac{1}{8}$ would both make $\frac{7}{8}$, but only $\frac{4}{8} + \frac{2}{8} + \frac{1}{8}$ will cancel down to unit fractions. So the Egyptians could write $\frac{7}{8}$ as $\frac{1}{2} + \frac{1}{4} + \frac{1}{8}$.

MISSION FILE 5:6

Math-e-magics involves logic problems. These problems are easy to solve if you can use algebra. Algebra uses letters instead of numbers. Try to choose letters that are related to what the number represents (for example, 'A' for age and 'M' for month). Think about where brackets might help you write down your algebra. For example, your age plus 5, times 2 would be 2(A+5).

MISSION FILE 5:7

For the Da Vinci files, you might find it useful to remember that angles that make a complete turn always add up to 360°:

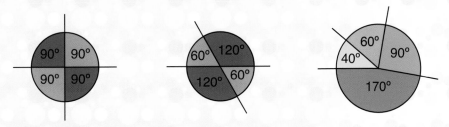

MISSION FILE 5:8

Probability is the chance that something will happen. Probabilities are often written as fractions and these are what are needed in this Mission. A $\frac{2}{7}$ probability means that you expect something to happen 2 times out of 7. The rules of probability are simple once you have found them. They are also the foundation of most the probability work you will ever do, so try to remember them.

MISSION FILE 5:9

You are looking for the relationship between the number of the day (or week) and the number of beetles there are. You need to find a process that works every day (or week). Remember to think about multiples, squares and differences when looking for the relationships. A good strategy is to keep multiplying up the day numbers until the difference between the day number and the number of beetles is the same every day.

The TASC Problem Solving Wheel

TASC: Thinking Actively in a Social Context

Learn from experience

Reflect
What have I learned?

Communicate
Who can I tell?

Evaluate
Did I succeed? Can I think of another way?

Implement
Now let me do it!

Communicate

Learn from experience

What have I learned?

Let's tell someone.

How well did I do?

Let's do it!

Evaluate

Implement

TA

We can learn to be expert thinkers!

Gather/organise

What do I know about this?

What is the task?

Identify

S C

How many ideas can I think of?

Generate

Which is the best idea?

Decide

Gather and Organise
What do I already know about this?

Identify
What am I trying to do?

Generate
How many ways can I do this?

Decide
Which is the best way?

TASC: Thinking Actively in a Social Context © Belle Wallace 2004

nace

What is NACE?

NACE is a charity which was set up in 1984. It is an organisation that supports the teaching of 'more-able' pupils and helps all children find out what they are good at and to do their best.

What does NACE do?

NACE helps teachers by giving them advice, books, materials and training. Many teachers, headteachers, parents and governors join NACE. Members of NACE can use a special website which gives them useful advice, ideas and materials to help children to learn.

NACE helps thousands of schools and teachers every year. It also helps teachers and children in other countries, such as America and China.

How will this book help me?

Brain Academy Supermaths books challenge and help you to become better at learning and a better mathematician by:
• Thinking of and testing different solutions to problems
• Making connections to what you already know
• Making mistakes and learning from them
• Working with your teacher, by yourself and with others
• Expecting you to get better and to go on to the next book
• Learning skills which you can use in other subjects and out of school

We hope that you enjoy the books!

Write to **RISING STARS** and let us know how the books helped you to learn and what you would like to see in the next books.

Rising Stars UK Ltd, 7 Hatchers Mews, Bermondsey Street, London SE1 3GS